In this comic ...

Batman

Blue Beetle is a normal boy who can transform!

The baddies are from an online game.

The Thinker is the chief baddie.

3

Meanwhile ...

But Blue Beetle and Batman were quicker ...

Stop! Don't you know that stealing is wrong?

Why are you here?

Go back to where you came from.

You are just a kid!

Don't ever say that!

Calling all players! Fight the Thinker! Smash his Power Helmet!

All over the planet, the players help.

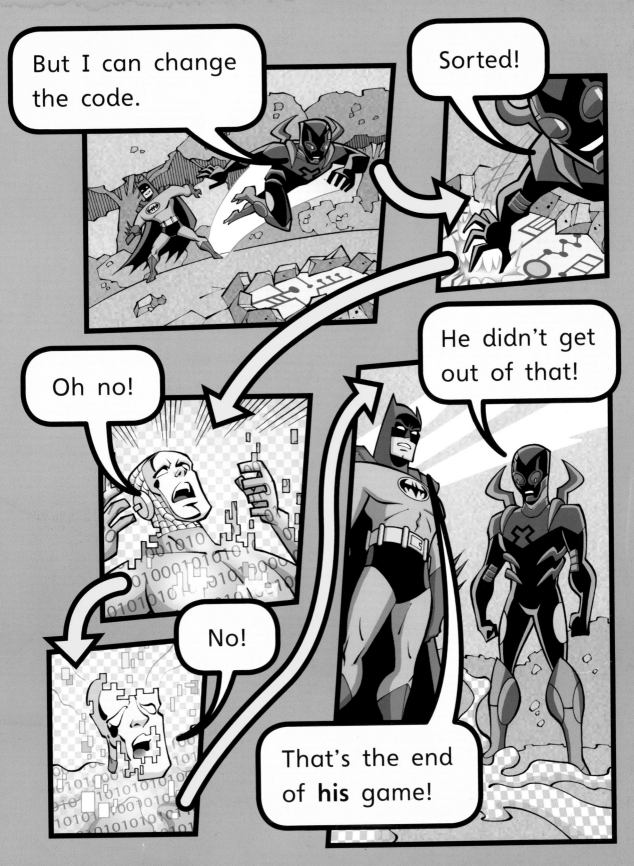